KT-405-764

840000728562

To Sarah Hart, who is building
'castles' for the kingdom
R. C.

To my mom, Queen of Big Mugs,
and in loving memory of my dad,
King of The Orange Handled Scissors
T. F.

First published 2021 by Nosy Crow Ltd
The Crow's Nest, 14 Baden Place, Crosby Row
London, SE1 1YW

www.nosycrow.com

ISBN 978 0 85763 967 7 (HB)
ISBN 978 1 78800 659 0 (PB)

'The National Trust' and the oak leaf logo are registered trademarks of The National Trust
(Enterprises) Limited (a subsidiary of The National Trust for Places of Historic Interest
or Natural Beauty, Registered Charity Number 205846).

Nosy Crow and associated logos are trademarks
and/or registered trademarks of Nosy Crow Ltd.

Text © Rebecca Colby 2021
Illustrations © Tom Froese 2021

The right of Rebecca Colby to be identified as the author and Tom Froese
to be identified as the illustrator of this work has been asserted.

All rights reserved.

This book is sold subject to the condition that it shall not,
by way of trade or otherwise, be lent, hired out or otherwise circulated in
any form of binding or cover other than that in which it is published.
No part of this publication may be reproduced, stored in a retrieval system,
or transmitted in any form or by any means
(electronic, mechanical, photocopying, recording or otherwise)
without the prior written permission of Nosy Crow Ltd.

A CIP catalogue record for this book is available from the British Library.

Printed in China.
Papers used by Nosy Crow are made from wood
grown in sustainable forests.

1 3 5 7 9 8 6 4 2 (HB)
1 3 5 7 9 8 6 4 2 (PB)

# THE CASTLE THE KING BUILT

Rebecca Colby • Tom Froese

These are the masons
who cut blocks of stone,

laying and carving
the walls 'round the throne . . .

inside the castle the King built.

These are the carpenters
sawing the poles,

hammering in nails
and drilling out holes . . .

inside the castle the King built.

This is the blacksmith
in front of his wheel,

shaping the iron
and sharpening steel . . .

inside the castle the King built.

These are the grooms
with handfuls of oats,

feeding the horses
and brushing
their coats . . .

inside the castle
the King built.

These are the knights as they fight in the fields,
training for war with their armour and shields . . .

inside the castle the King built.

These are the merchants
who sell cloth and spices,

arranging their carpets
and yelling out prices . . .

inside the castle the King built.

These are the bakers
with flour and yeast,

kneading the dough
to make sweets for the feast . . .

inside the castle the King built.

These are the servants presenting each dish,
carrying venison, partridge and fish . . .

inside the castle the King built.

These are the minstrels
who sing by the fire,

piping and drumming
and strumming a lyre . . .

inside the castle the King built.

Here is the King
with a sword in his hand,

supporting the people
and ruling the land . . .

. . . inside the castle they ALL built!

**Mason**

**Carpenter**

**Blacksmith**

**Groom**

**Knight**

**Merchant**

**Baker**

**Servant**

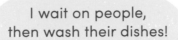

**Minstrel**

**King**

Unlike today, it was almost all men living inside the castle during medieval times.

The King's wife and daughters would have lived there with their servants and companions, but apart from that, the only women in the castle were female servants, nurses or perhaps laundry maids.